The Greatest Story Ever Told

By Kim Blauwkamp

Illustrated by Tracy Yonker

KAIROS
Ministries

The Greatest Story Ever Told
by Kim Blauwkamp

Published by:
Kairos Ministries
P.O. Box 0093
Jenison, MI 49429-0093
616-667-9106
www.ministerioskairos.org

Cover design: Tracy Yonker

ISBN 0-9724379-0-8
1 2 3 4 5 Edition/Year 06 05 04 03 02

Printed in Colombia

Dedicated...

To the Lord Jesus Christ. We give Him the glory for He has done exceedingly above and beyond all that we can ask for or think.

Our prayer is that He will be glorified and as this book reaches out, may it touch the lives of those who read it.

INTRODUCTION

Let's celebrate the greatest story ever told. This story is about the birth of Jesus. It is a story about love. A love that wants to touch a heart, change a life, and restore a family. It is a love that came to the little town of Bethlehem on that first Christmas morning. The Bible says in John 3:16 that God loves you so much that He sent His one and only Son so that when you believe in Him you will not perish, but have eternal life. Jesus is that gift of love sent from the Father above. So let's celebrate the birth of Jesus...*the greatest story ever told.*

You can find the Bible narration in Luke 1:26-38; 2:1-20; and Matthew 1:18-2:12.

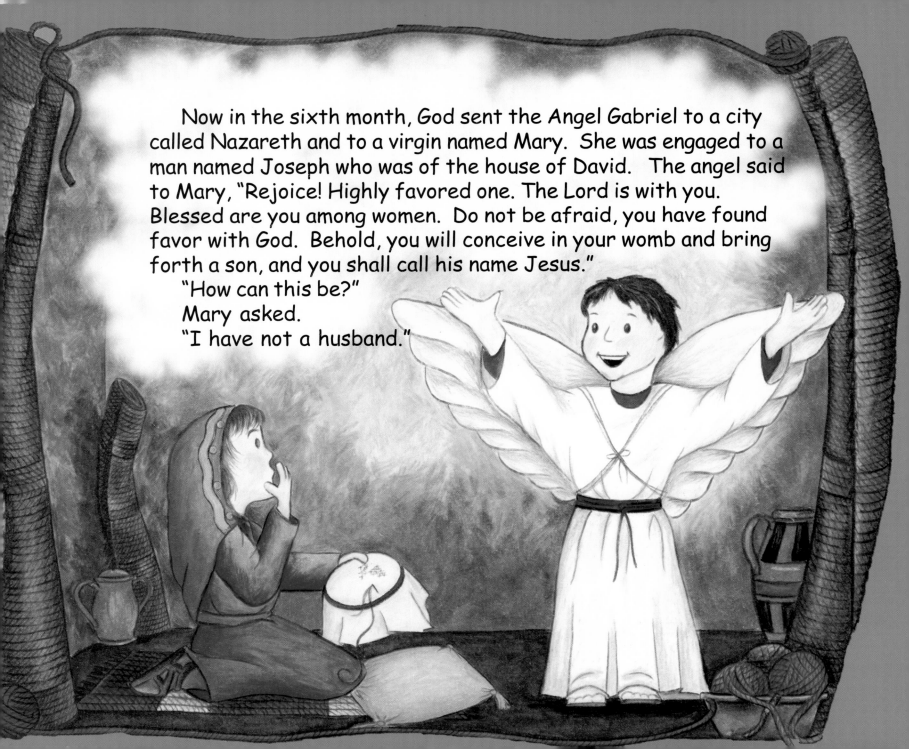

Now in the sixth month, God sent the Angel Gabriel to a city called Nazareth and to a virgin named Mary. She was engaged to a man named Joseph who was of the house of David. The angel said to Mary, "Rejoice! Highly favored one. The Lord is with you. Blessed are you among women. Do not be afraid, you have found favor with God. Behold, you will conceive in your womb and bring forth a son, and you shall call his name Jesus."

"How can this be?"

Mary asked.

"I have not a husband."

The angel answered, "The power of the Most High will cover you. This Holy Child born to you will be called the Son of God."

"Praise God, I am the maidservant of the Lord," answered Mary. "I am willing to fulfill His plan for my life. May it be done to me according to Thy word."

Now the angel departed, and Mary was found to be with child of the Holy Spirit.

Now Joseph who was engaged to Mary, found out that Mary was going to have a baby. Being a just man, Joseph decided to break the engagement secretly. While he was considering this, an angel came to him in a dream saying, "Joseph, son of David, do not be afraid to take Mary as your wife, because what is conceived in her is of the Holy Spirit. She will bring forth a son, and you shall call His name Jesus. He shall save His people from their sins."

After hearing the message from the Lord, Joseph went to Mary and told her what the angel had said. Then Mary and Joseph became husband and wife as the angel of the Lord commanded.

In those days, Caesar Augustus of Rome declared a very important law; a law that would affect the whole world. Roman soldiers sent from Caesar went forth saying, "Hear ye! Hear ye! Fine people of Nazareth; I have a very important message sent from Caesar Augustus. It has been ordered: every person of every family should return to their hometown to be counted and taxed."

Mary and Joseph left Nazareth and traveled to Bethlehem, because Joseph was of the family line of David.

As they entered Bethlehem, it was about time for Mary to have her baby, and they needed a place to stay. So they made their way to an inn.

As Joseph came to the inn, he knocked on the door and said, "Hello. Do you have a room for us? My wife Mary is about to have a baby."

"I am sorry. There is just no room," said the inn keeper. "Since Caesar declared everyone to be counted and taxed, people have been looking for rooms everywhere. Maybe down the street they can take you in."

Mary and Joseph made their way to the next inn. Again they asked, "Do you have any rooms?"

"I am so sorry. I know you and your wife have traveled many miles, but there is just no room.... Hey! Wait a minute. We do have a stable out back. It's not much, but it is warm."

"This is an answer from the Lord. We will take it! Thank you very much," responded Joseph.

"Here, let us help you. We will show you the way," said the inn keeper's wife.

After the long trip from Nazareth, the Lord provided a place for Mary and Joseph to stay. The kind inn keeper led them to a lowly stable. That night truly became the night of all nights. For Mary gave birth to her first born son, and she wrapped him in swaddling clothes and laid him in the manger. They gave him the name, JESUS!

The heavens rejoiced when Jesus was born. That special day would be the most celebrated day throughout all the ages. It was the birthday of Jesus, the Savior and King!

In the same country there were shepherds keeping watch over their flocks by night. The angel of the Lord appeared to them, and the glory of the Lord shone around them. They were greatly afraid.

The angel said, "Do not be afraid. I bring you WONDERFUL, AWESOME, GLORIOUS NEWS OF GREAT JOY which will be to all people. For there is born to you in the city of David, a Savior. He is Christ the Lord! You shall find the baby wrapped in swaddling clothes, lying in a manger."

Suddenly, there was with the angel a multitude of heavenly hosts praising God and saying, "Glory to God in the highest and on earth, peace and goodwill to all men."

As the angels departed, one shepherd said, "Can you believe this? We have just seen angels. Christ the Savior has been born.

Let's go to Bethlehem to see what has happened!"

The shepherds left their flocks and hurried as fast as they could to the little town of Bethlehem. They found the baby wrapped in swaddling clothes and lying in a manger.

In amazement they bowed down and worshipped Jesus, their Savior and King.

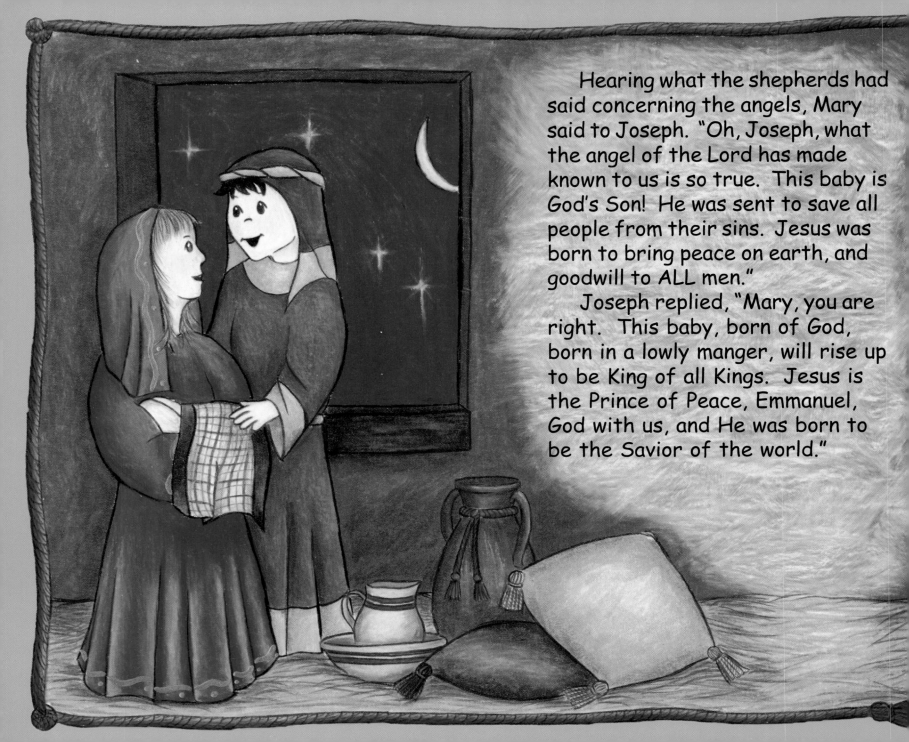

Hearing what the shepherds had said concerning the angels, Mary said to Joseph. "Oh, Joseph, what the angel of the Lord has made known to us is so true. This baby is God's Son! He was sent to save all people from their sins. Jesus was born to bring peace on earth, and goodwill to ALL men."

Joseph replied, "Mary, you are right. This baby, born of God, born in a lowly manger, will rise up to be King of all Kings. Jesus is the Prince of Peace, Emmanuel, God with us, and He was born to be the Savior of the world."

Sometime later, three wise men from the East went to worship the King. They followed the bright star that the Lord had set before them. The star led them to Bethlehem, then stopped and stayed over the place where Jesus was. When they saw this, the wise men rejoiced with exceeding great joy. They entered the place and presented their gifts to Jesus.

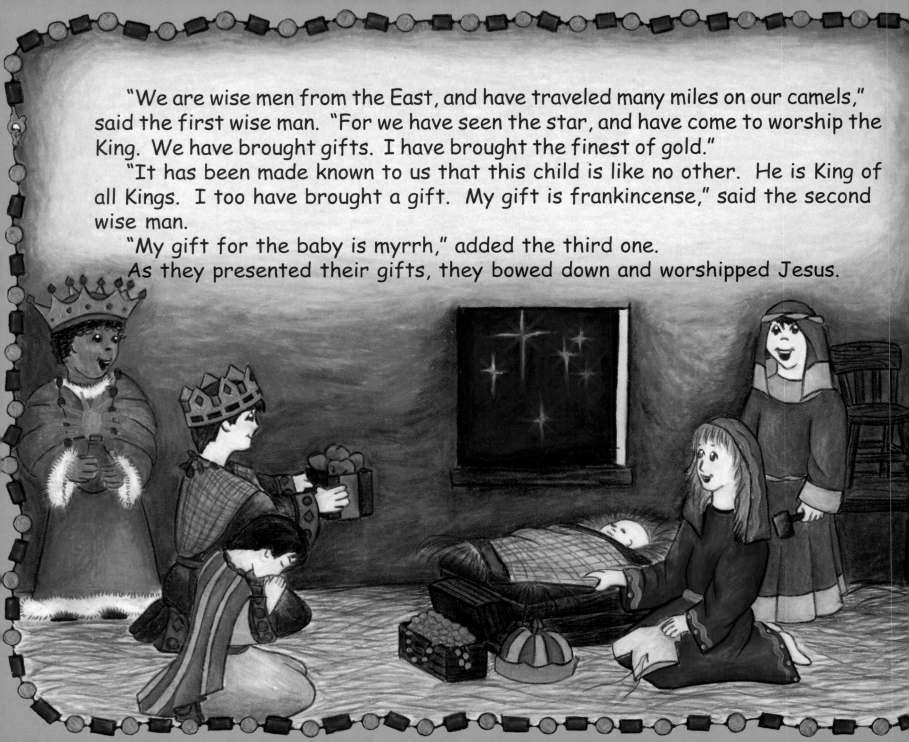

"We are wise men from the East, and have traveled many miles on our camels," said the first wise man. "For we have seen the star, and have come to worship the King. We have brought gifts. I have brought the finest of gold."

"It has been made known to us that this child is like no other. He is King of all Kings. I too have brought a gift. My gift is frankincense," said the second wise man.

"My gift for the baby is myrrh," added the third one.

As they presented their gifts, they bowed down and worshipped Jesus.

The wise men, shepherds, and angels gave praise and glory to Jesus. We can also worship God by believing that Jesus was sent to earth to be our Savior. Jesus went to the cross and shed His blood to pay for our sins. When we believe this, our sins will be forgiven, and our hearts will be filled with the true meaning of Christmas. We will be filled with peace on earth, and goodwill to all men. Our hearts will be filled with JOY!

C H R I S

What does Christmas really mean?
Look and listen and you will see.
The letters of Christmas they will tell
The meaning of Christmas very well.

C

C is for *Christmas*
Jesus is the light
Born in the town of Bethlehem
That special Christmas night.

T M A S

H

H is for *heaven*
A gift from heaven above
Jesus is that gift
A package filled with love.

R is for *rejoice*
The shepherds did that night
They heard the news of Jesus
It filled them with delight.

R

C H R I S

I is for **invite**
Invite the Lord Jesus in
He'll cleanse your heart from evil
And take away your sin.

S is for the **stable**
The stable filled with hay
Jesus Son of Glory
In the manger He did lay.

T is for the **tree**
They nailed Him to the cross
If it hadn't been for Jesus
Our lives would be lost.

M is for the **magi**
Three kings they did come
To worship baby Jesus
God's one and only Son.

A is for the **angels**
And the message they did bring
That fills our lives with happiness
And makes us want to sing.

S is for the **Savior**
That special baby boy
He came to earth from heaven
To fill us with His JOY!

If you want this joy...

If you want all that the Father wants to give you through the gift of Jesus, say this prayer now and ask Jesus to come rule in your heart.

"God, I believe You love me and Jesus was born to be my Savior. I believe He went to the cross to shed His blood for all my sins. I believe He rose again, defeating death, sin and the devil, so I can have eternal life. Father God, forgive me for all my sins. May the love of Jesus, through the power of the Holy Spirit, come into my heart right now. I confess with my mouth that Jesus is my Savior and my Lord. In Jesus' name, AMEN!"

If you've just prayed this prayer, you are saved; and there is another celebration going on in Heaven, just for you!

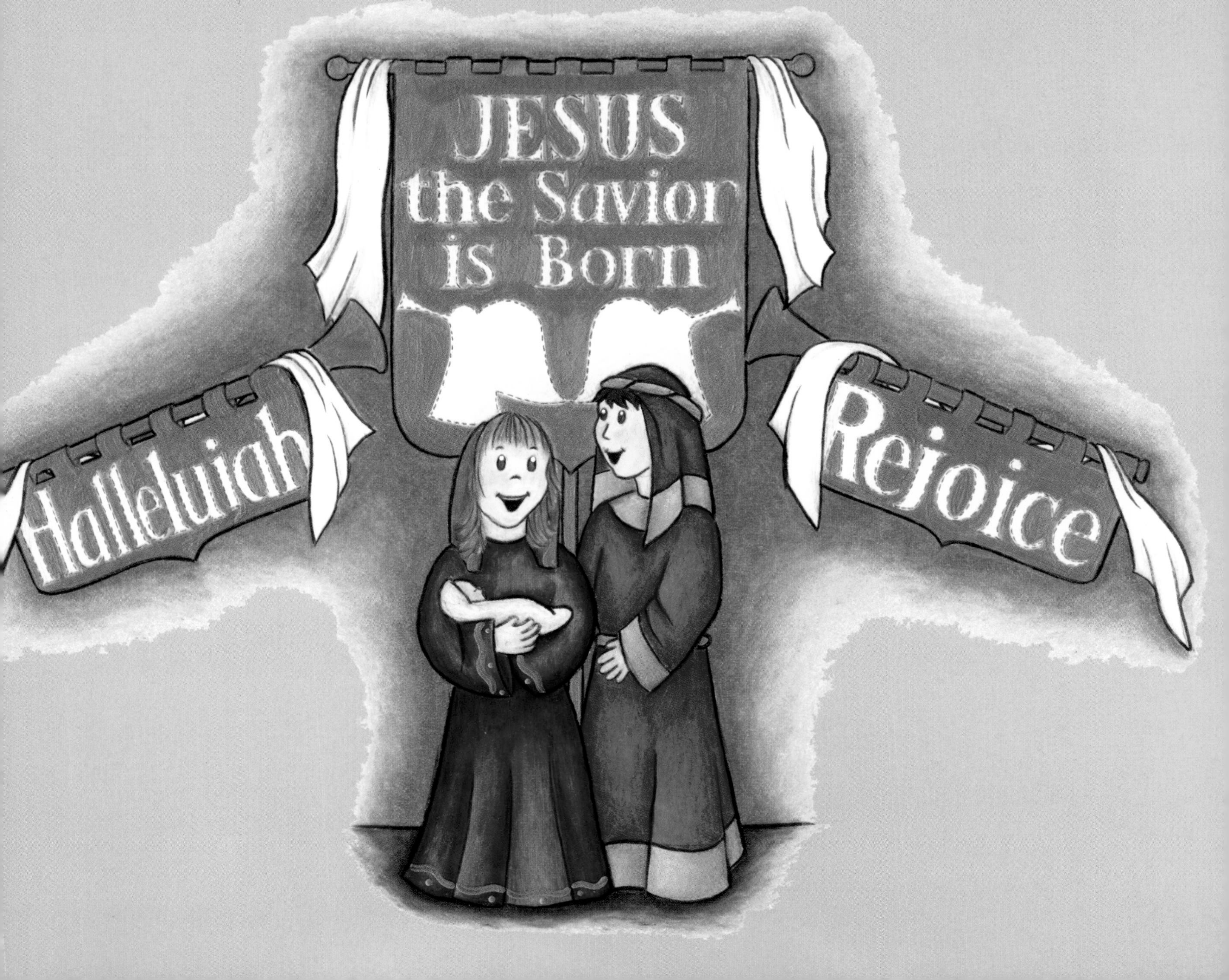
JESUS
the Savior
is Born
Halleluiah
Rejoice

Resurrection Life Church of Grandville, Michigan, under the leadership of senior Pastor Duane Vander Klok, exists to develop totally committed followers of Jesus Christ to reach a lost and dying world. We accomplish this by:

    *Ministering the Word of God.

    *Ministering to God through praise and worship.

    *Ministering to children and youth.

    *Ministering to the world through missions.

If you have prayed the prayer in this book,
and would like more information, please contact us at:

Resurrection Life Church
5100 Ivanrest SW
Grandville, MI 49418
Tel: 616-534-4923
www.reslife.org